P9-CDF-729

GILGAMESH

GILGAMESH

Man's First Story

written and illustrated by

BERNARDA BRYSON

HOLT, RINEHART & WINSTON NEW YORK CHICAGO SAN FRANCISCO

Published simultaneously in Canada by Holt, Rinehart
and Winston of Canada, Limited.
Library of Congress Catalog Card Number: 66-11420
First Edition
91131-0117
Printed by Brüder Rosenbaum in Vienna, Austria,
in association with Chanticleer Press, Inc.

To Abby

CONTENTS

PART ONE

The Temper of the Gods

PART TWO

The Wanderings of Gilgamesh

PART ONE

The Temper of the Gods

THE WORLD OF GILGAMESH

THE MOUNTAINS WITHOUT END where, after a distance of three biru (double hours) the sun can no longer be seen

THE BITTER RIVER

MOUNTAINS OF MASHU

BABYLON

URUK

EUPHRATES RIVER

THE GREAT SALT SWAMP

THE BITTER RIVER

THE SEA-WITHOUT-END whence arose the animals: the tiger, the he-goat, the gazelle, the panther, the lion, the hyena, the antelope and the wild horse during the Year of the Great Serpent at the time of the flood

Uruk-of-the-Walls

The world of Gilgamesh was hemmed in by the mighty mountains of Mashu that were the edge between day and night. It was circled by the Bitter River that flowed round and round it unceasingly, and that had no beginning and no end. No one knew what lay beyond the river, since the very touch of its waters was death. Some speculated that to the north of it lay the mountains-without-end and to the south, the sea-without-end, but still no one was sure.

To the west was the void into which the sun set. There opened those rocky caverns through which the sun passed under the earth and back into the Eastern Garden where his home was and whence he arose again in the mornings. So much was known.

The gods of Gilgamesh were almost everywhere: There was great Anu of the skies and Ea who ruled over the deep waters. There was Enlil whose domain was the earth, and mighty Ishtar the goddess of love, so amiable in her friendship, so terrible in her wrath. There was Shamash, the sun and Sin, the moon, and Adad whose voice was the thunder. And there were many other gods whom we shall certainly come across from time to time.

The city of Gilgamesh was Uruk-of-the-Walls. This was the most splendid of all the seven cities of Sumer, and Gilgamesh was its king. Uruk was a city of many-colored temples, of brick houses, marketplaces, and open groves of trees. Its towering walls protected it from all sorts of evil, from the armies of enemy kings, from floods, from wild beasts too, and unfriendly gods; but most of all they protected it from the monster Humbaba who lived on a nearby mountain and who constantly breathed fire and smoke and soot into the sky.

It is with the walls of Uruk that our story begins:

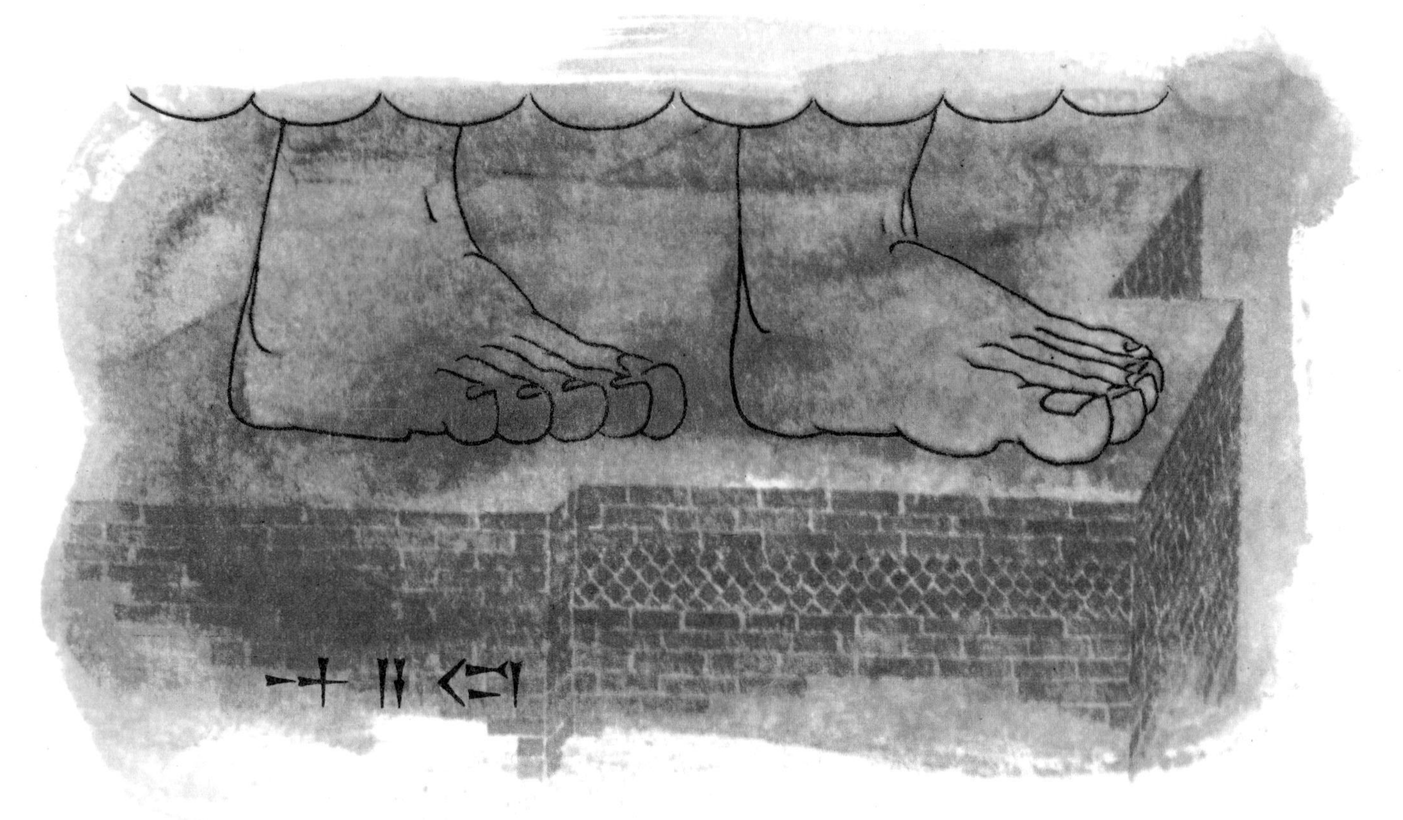

On a certain morning, a company of elders of the city mounted to the very highest level of the walls, and there they met in secret with a number of the most powerful gods.

The eldest and most eminent of the elders approached with folded hands toward the god, Anu. He bowed: "O Father Anu, we have come to complain!"

"It is about Gilgamesh the King," said a second elder.

A third spoke, "He continues to build the city walls higher and ever higher, yet who has need of such high walls?"

"It has become a heavy burden," said a fourth. "We want to rest!"

"Mothers no longer see their sons, nor fathers either, for that matter. Our girls languish without lovers; marriages have ceased. We do nothing but build, build, build!"

"Wine sellers cannot sell their wines; the musicians are idle; and there is no gayety!"

"And no business, and no leisure!"

"We ourselves rather like the high walls," said one of the gods. "We often come and crouch here at night and watch the goings-on of mortals. It's very entertaining!"

"Father Anu, you must help us! You must punish Gilgamesh!"

"What do you want me to do?" asked Anu. "Do you want me to throw rocks out of Heaven at the King?"

"Not at all, not that!"

"Go away," said Anu. "I like Gilgamesh. He is a very fine fellow and perfectly fearless. He wrestles with lions; he tames them with his bare hands—I've seen him. Besides I have heard that he is himself partly god. I am quite sure that if he wants to build the walls higher, he knows best!"

But the goddess Ishtar thought otherwise. "Father, listen to them; help them! I will not see my young girls left without lovers! I will not see my mothers bereft of their sons!"

"Indeed," said the eldest of the elders, "perhaps you will listen to our plan, for we do have a plan!"

"It's this," interrupted a second elder. "We want you to create a man—"

"A man taller even than Gilgamesh—"

"And more powerful!" another cried eagerly.

"A wild beast of a man," a small elder said, "unconquerable!"

"Who will come to earth, to the city here, and attack the King—"

"And destroy him!" they all shouted at once.

As the elders explained their plan, the goddess Ishtar made a sign toward another goddess named Aruru, she who was responsible for the shaping of human forms. Aruru reached down to the earth and scooped up in her hand a huge lump of clay. This, she began to model and shape, spitting on it from time to time in order to keep it soft and malleable.

And as the gods disputed the matter this way and that, Aruru made the clay into the form of a man, one so like Gilgamesh that he could have been his brother. But this man was unkempt and savage in his looks, and from his head there arose two majestic horns like those of some wild beast.

By the time Father Anu had given in to the elders and to the pleas of Ishtar, the form of the man was complete. Aruru then carried him in her arms into the depths of a cedar forest and laid him on the earth. And this was Enkidu.

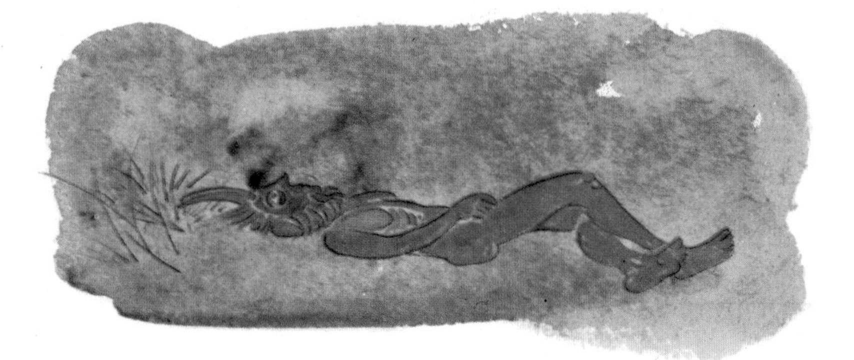

He slept there on the earth for some time and then wakened and looked around him. He didn't know who he was or where he had come from.

Suddenly its yellow eyes looked at him, and before he could run the beast had leaped on him. He felt its terrible claws rip into the flesh along his sides. Enkidu cried out with pain.

But then he wrestled with this animal, his first enemy. He first felt anger and the mighty strength of his muscles. He bent the lion backward, he twisted its neck. They fell to the ground each trying to kill the other. Enkidu grasped the neck and the back leg of the beast; he wrenched its back and saw the great creature lie writhing and roaring on the earth. There was foam around its mouth; the tongue rolled sidewise and hung piteously out of the beast's mouth. Enkidu knew that it was thirsty; he felt pity and he carried water in his hands to slake the animal's thirst. Then he washed away the blood from its wounds, caressed its mane and watched over it through the night. In the morning the lion limped away, but it returned again and again, and it too became Enkidu's friend.

The Luring of Enkidu

A young hunter ran into the hut of his father, a shepherd, and hid himself in a corner.

"What's wrong with you?" his father shouted. "Why do you behave like that?"

The hunter opened his mouth and cried out, "O father, there is a strange man I've seen in the forest and wandering over the steppes. How many times have I complained to you that my traps were broken and robbed! Well, today I saw the thief—a terrifying sight, father, a man whose strength is like that of the hosts of heaven! He filled the pits that I had dug. He broke open my traps. He freed the animals; he carried them off as a mother lion might carry off her whelps!"

"Come, come!" said the shepherd. "You're seeing things, son! The game is scarce; you've been careless with your traps!"

"The hair springs out of his head like a field of grain, and he has the horns of a wild beast!"

"If he stole your catch of game, my son, why didn't you stop him?"

"He is taller and more powerful than Gilgamesh the King. I was numbed with fear!"

"If what you say is true, son, then we must report the matter to the King. But if you have lied, we will be in disgrace forever!"

The shepherd and his son went into the city of Uruk to make their complaint. But there the populace were already spreading rumors about the wild man. Some said, "He is covered with hair from head to foot," and others, "He is taller than a giant and eats grass with the gazelles!"

It was the eldest of the elders who led the hunter and his father before the King. "O Gilgamesh," said the elder, "there is a wild man that terrorizes the countryside. He robs the hunter of his game and disperses the herds of the shepherd. He turns all who see him numb with fear—indeed I've heard that he is taller and more powerful than Gilgamesh the King!"

Gilgamesh, who feared nothing, might have been expected to say, "Then it's I who will go out and subdue him and bring him captive to the city!" Not at all; he sent to the temple of Ishtar for a certain priestess, one called Harim, servant of the goddess.

He said to her, "Harim, I have a certain task for you; it is one that turns the boldest hunters numb with fear!"

"Then I am afraid," said Harim.

The eldest of the elders spoke angrily, "This is not a girl's task, O King; it is a task for a brave man—a hero!"

"Tut tut," said Gilgamesh. "It is a girl's task of smiles and charm. Go, Harim; soften the heart of the wild man and bring him back to the city!"

Harim was led by the hunter to the edge of the forest, and she noted that he began to tremble with fear. "Go back to the hut of your father," she commanded. "If I can tame the wild man, I will lead him into the city alone."

The hunter was shamed by the girl's bravery. "Do not enter the forest, O Harim; I myself will go." But the priestess laughed at him and sent him home.

She went among the dark cedars; she listened to the sounds of birds and of monkeys chattering. She noted the bits of sunlight that filtered through the branches and lit up flowers, moss, and bracken on the forest floor. "How peaceful a place this is! How could any evil thing lurk here?" Harim found a fresh spring bubbling with cool water. She sat beside it on a stone, untied her sandals, and dipped her feet in the water.

Enkidu came to the place with the small wild horse and the gazelle. As they drew near, the two beasts became nervous, sniffed the air, and fled. But Enkidu stood still; he wondered what new danger was near, what unknown beast might have come to the water.

When he saw the girl sitting there his breath failed and he was overcome. He had not yet seen a human being, and this creature seemed to him the most admirable, the most enchanting being that he had ever seen. He stood quietly in order not to frighten her.

Harim gazed at his giant figure, his soaring horns, and his unkempt looks and would have run away, but she could not move. She opened her mouth to scream and could not make a sound. She was numb with terror. And Enkidu noting this remained quiet; he had made friends with many timid creatures and he knew their ways.

When the priestess saw the gentleness of his manner, her courage returned to her somewhat. She called out shyly, "Hello!"

Enkidu knew no words. He could babble somewhat as the monkeys did. He could bark quite like a fox, or trill like many birds. He had various calls of greeting for his wild friends, but this new animal made sounds that he could not understand.

He neither barked nor roared, but stood perplexed looking at the girl. Again she spoke, and now held out her hands to him in greeting.

Enkidu approached slowly and sat on the earth beside the white feet of Harim. She said all sorts of things to him and he understood nothing. She asked him many questions and he could not reply. But he felt ecstasy in his heart, and great contentment in merely sitting beside her.

How easy was her conquest of Enkidu! Harim smiled, but she now began to feel a new sort of fear. How could she lead this great fellow, so gentle and so innocent, back to the city of Uruk? Would the people set on him and kill him? Would they jeer at him? Would the King have him put into a cage and carried through the streets on the backs of soldiers? She shuddered.

No, first she must teach him the ways of people, the conformity of life.

"*Al-ka ti-ba i-na ĝa-aĝ-ĝa-ri!*" said Harim. "Come, rise from the ground!" But the wild man did not understand. Thus, she taught him the word for standing, and then after that, the word for sitting. She taught him the words for walking, running, talking, laughing, eating, and he repeated each one, learning it. She taught him the words for trees and for stones and for water, for earth and for the trailing vines that grew beside the spring, and for the spring itself. She taught him the words for feet and hands and the names of all the fingers and all the myriad words of love.

Thus patiently, Harim taught Enkidu to be like ordinary men. She cut his hair and combed it in the way of people of the city. She made him bathe; she tore her long tunic into two parts, making of one-half a garment for Enkidu, keeping the other half for herself.

Again she spoke to him, and now he understood, "*A-na-tal-ka En-ki-du ki-ma ili ta-ba-as-si!*"—"I gaze upon you, Enkidu; you are like a god!"

He brought her gifts—all the things that he had come to know and love in the forest and from the open steppes; wild cucumbers and cassia melon, grapes and figs and caper buds from the dry rocks. He brought her blossoms of golden mimosa and fragrant branches of jasmine.

After some time had passed Harim said, "Now I will lead Enkidu out among the people and everyone will admire him!" But still she feared for his life so she took him first to the hut of the shepherd.

At the edge of the forest Enkidu stopped and turned back. He was overcome with regret; how could he leave forever his friends of the woods and wild places? Who would protect them? Who would release them from the traps? How could he leave behind his friend the little wild horse, or the gazelle, the rabbits, the monkeys that had taught him to play games?

But as he approached they leaped away startled. The rabbit hid trembling in the grass and the birds took off with a wild flutter of wings.

Enkidu threw himself to the ground, weeping. "O Harim, what

have I done? How have I made all my friends into strangers? Why do they run from me?"

"Enkidu is no longer a wild creature. He is no longer a beast of the forest and the open plain. Enkidu is now a man. He will live among men and be eminent among men!"

Enkidu followed regretfully as the priestess led him toward the hut of the shepherd. This man greeted him with awe and admiration, but his son fled from the place and hid in the sheepfold. After some time he returned, running. "Father, a lion has entered the fold! It is devouring the lambs!"

Enkidu went to the sheepfold where again he wrestled with the lion, his friend who no longer knew him. Again he overcame the beast, but he let it go free. He lifted the lambs gently, washing and tending the ones that bled. To his great joy they did not shun him or run away. Neither did the young calves nor the barnyard fowl. A dog followed him wagging its tail. A cat smoothed its fur against his legs, and again he was content.

In the hut of the shepherd Enkidu learned to sit on a chair and to wash his hands before eating. He learned how to care for animals, to make plants grow, and to build with mud and brick and reeds. He learned to play on a flute. He ate bread. There he tasted the strong sesame wine and drank seven cups. His face shone, he rejoiced; he sang.

Harim smiled. "Now Enkidu has become like a man, we shall go into the city!"

The First Dream

The mother of Gilgamesh was the pale Ninsun, herself listed among the goddesses, a gentle queen who had the gift of prophecy and could read dreams.

Gilgamesh came to her, troubled, sat beside her, and put his head in her lap. "Mother, I've had a curious dream."

Ninsun caressed the hair that sprang from his head like a field of grain. "How did the dream go?"

"Like this: I was walking through the streets of the city. As I drew near the temple of Ishtar, the sky opened up and an axe with double edges was hurled downward at me. I dodged, but it came so close to striking me that I could feel the wind on my cheek. I fell, and the axe buried itself in the pavement at my side—When I wakened I was shivering!"

Ninsun closed her eyes and she too shivered. "I can tell you the meaning of the dream, O Gilgamesh. It is a warning, and you must do just as I tell you. . .

"The meaning of the dream: the axe with double edges—that is a man as like to you as a brother, as like as one edge of the axe is to the other. But the axe is a weapon of battle, O my son, and in your dream you fell! All this is an evil portent. Do not walk in the streets! Do not go into the open places! Do not approach the temple of Ishtar! Meanwhile, O Gilgamesh, I will make offerings to the gods; I will appease them!"

But Gilgamesh laughed. "I am not afraid Ninsun, dear Mother! Am I not two parts god and only one part man? Why then should I be afraid of any man? Why should I fear the open places?"

The people fell back, appalled. However tall and powerful this wild man might be, how did he dare to cross the path of the King? Was not Gilgamesh, after all, equally tall and equally powerful?

Gilgamesh tried to brush aside the insolent fellow, but Enkidu leaped upon him like a wild bull. They grappled with each other; they destroyed the threshold; they demolished the wall. It seemed that each was as powerful as the other, and each as angry. They fought, they wrestled; the round pillar of the gateway crumbled, scattering its colored tiles across the street. Bricks and mortar were loosened, and everywhere was the dust of battle.

Enkidu sought to bend the back of the King as he had twice wrenched that of the lion, but the King was more powerful and did not yield. He, on the other hand, caught hold of the soaring horns of Enkidu and held him fast, slowly twisting his neck. But Enkidu broke away and again they lunged at each other. Which one would destroy the other? The populace surged around them and would have interfered to save their king, but the elders of the town cautioned them: "Stand back; the King will subdue the wild man; your help would only shame him!"

Now the King seemed to prevail, and now the wild man. They sweat, they bled, and neither seemed to weaken. Harim came to the temple gate and drew back again, her heart failing her.

Gilgamesh, the lofty and unconquerable, weakened and fell to his knees. Again the crowd surged forward to help him, but the elders cried out: "Stop! Whatever happens is the will of the gods!"

But even as Gilgamesh sank to his knees, his spear rested upon his back, and his stone axe remained at his side untouched.

He knelt helpless, his breast exposed to the fury of the wild man, when strangely enough, Enkidu lifted him to his feet. They clasped hands, they embraced.

"I salute you, Gilgamesh, lion and great fighter!"

"Welcome to my city, O godlike Enkidu!"

They thereupon pledged eternal friendship, the King and the wild man from the steppes who had been sent by the gods to destroy him.

The elders of Uruk stared at each other, wondering.

The Monster Humbaba

Perfect was the friendship of Gilgamesh and Enkidu. The wild man asked only to be the servant of the King, but Gilgamesh called him "my younger brother," and Ninsun, the queen looked upon him almost as a son. Everywhere, they went together and everywhere they were admired. They took part in feats of strength and daring, winning all prizes and all praise. And in all this Enkidu was content.

Not so, Gilgamesh. On one occasion he said to his friend, "Day and night I dream of a great enterprise. Whenever I close my eyes, voices come to me and say: 'Arouse yourself, Gilgamesh, there are great things to be done!' "

Enkidu's mind was full of foreboding.

"You and I, Enkidu, we will climb the mountain and destroy the monster Humbaba!"

Enkidu's eyes filled with tears and he turned away.

"Why should you cry, O Enkidu? Are you not the bravest of men? Are you no longer my friend and brother whom I admire more than anyone at all?"

Enkidu spoke: "I knew the presence of Humbaba even when I was a wild man on the steppes and in the forest. I could hear the sighing of his voice rise over the sound of thunder and high winds. I could hear the beating of his heart and feel the heat of his breath at a distance of five-hundred shar. I do not fear beast or mortal man, O Gilgamesh, but Humbaba is not mortal; he is the appointed servant of the gods, the guardian of the wild cows and the cedar forest. Whoever comes near him will grow weak. He will become paralyzed and will fail."

"The monster is an everlasting evil," said Gilgamesh. "It oppresses the people. Day and night it spreads fires and spews its ashes over the town. It is hated by great Shamash, constantly obscuring his face. O Enkidu, shall my life be as an empty wind? What am I, if I turn aside from the things I want to do? I am nothing, only someone waiting for death! But if I do this thing, O Enkidu, even though I should fail, then they will say, 'Gilgamesh died a hero's death! He died defending his people.' I will have made an everlasting name for myself and my life will not be as an empty wind!"

Still Enkidu turned away.

Gilgamesh then called in the armorers, the makers of spears and shields and axes. They cast for him swords of bronze inlaid with silver and gold. They made powerful long-bows and arrows tipped with stone, and most beautiful of all, a spear with a handle of lapis lazuli and gold inset with many glittering jewels.

Gilgamesh called Enkidu and laid the weapons before him, hoping to tempt him with their beauty. And still Enkidu said no.

Gilgamesh was downcast. "My brother has grown soft and timid. He no longer loves daring; he has forgotten adventure; I will go alone!"

The elders of Uruk, who had long ago forgotten their hatred of the King, now came to him: "O Gilgamesh, do not undertake this thing. You are young; your heart has carried you away. Settle down, O King; take a bride to yourself; let your life be tranquil!"

Gilgamesh laughed. "Save your wise counsel for my friend, Enkidu. He'll listen. You waste your words on me, good fathers!"

The elders came in secret to Enkidu. "If the King stubbornly insists on doing this thing, risking danger and defying the gods, then Enkidu you must accompany him!"

"Indeed, you must go ahead of him," a second elder said, "for it is known that whoever first enters the cedar gate will be the first killed."

"Besides, it is you who know the way, Enkidu. It is you who have trodden the road!"

"May Shamash stand beside you!"

"May he open the path for you!"

Enkidu went to Gilgamesh. "My head is bowed, O King. I am your brother and your servant; wherever you will go, I will go."

Tears came into the eyes of Gilgamesh; his faith in Enkidu was restored. "Now, my brother, we will go to Ninsun; we will tell our plan and ask her to petition the gods for our success!"

Pale as she was, Ninsun turned more pale. But since she could not dissuade her son, she merely kissed him, giving him her blessing. To Enkidu she said, "Even though you are not my son, O Enkidu, you are like a son to me, and I shall petition the gods for you as for Gilgamesh. But remember, please, that as a man protects his own person, so must he guard the life of his companion!"

The people of Uruk walked with the two friends through the streets admiring their weapons and praising their bold plan: "Praise be to Gilgamesh who dares everything! Praise be to Enkidu who will safeguard his companion!" But Harim the priestess mourned, "May your feet carry you back safely to the city, Enkidu!" And thus they set out.

Ninsun dressed herself in her finest garments. She attached the golden pendants to her ears and set the divine tiara upon her head. She anointed herself with perfumes and carried in her hand an incense that would carry its pleasant odors into the sky. Mounting with stately grace to the roof of her palace, she raised her voice to its highest pitch and called out, "O Shamash, listen to me!" Then waiting a little for her voice to reach the ears of the god, she went on: "O Shamash, why have you given my son Gilgamesh such a restless heart? Why have you made him so eager for adventure? Now he has gone up to fight with the indestructible monster

Humbaba. Why have you sent him, O Shamash, to wipe out the evil that you abhor? It is all your plan! It is you who have planted the idea in his head! May you not sleep, O Shamash, until Gilgamesh and his friend Enkidu return to Uruk. If they fail, may you never sleep again!"

Ninsun extinguished the small blaze from under the incense and descended from the roof of the palace.

Gilgamesh and Enkidu walked toward the mountain of the cedar forest. At a distance of twenty double-hours they sat down beside the path and ate a small amount of food. At a distance of thirty double-hours, they lay down to sleep, covering themselves with their garments. On the following day they walked a distance of fifty double-hours. Within three days' time, they covered a distance that it would have taken ordinary men some fifteen days to cover. They reached the mountain and saw before them a towering and magnificent gate of cedar wood.

"Here," said Gilgamesh, "we must pour meal upon the earth, for that will gain us the goodwill of the gods; it will persuade them to reveal their purpose in our dreams!"

They poured meal on the ground and lay down to sleep. After some time Gilgamesh wakened his friend. "Enkidu, I have had a dream; it went like this: We were standing in a deep gorge beside a mountain. Compared to it, we were the size of flies! Before our very eyes the mountain collapsed; it fell in a heap!"

"The meaning of that seems very clear," said Enkidu. "It means that Humbaba is the mountain and that he will fall before us!"

They closed their eyes again and slept. After some time, Gilgamesh again awakened his friend. "I've had another dream, Enkidu. I saw the same mountain this time, and again it fell, but it fell on me. However, as I lay struggling, a beautiful personage appeared. He took me by my feet and dragged me out from under the mountain. Now I wonder what this means? Is it that you will rescue me from the monster, or will someone else come along?"

They pondered a little and went back to sleep. Next Enkidu wakened his brother, Gilgamesh. "Has a cold shower passed over us? Did the lightning strike fires, and was there a rain of ashes?"

"The earth is dry and clean," said Gilgamesh, "you must have dreamed!" But since neither of them could understand the meaning of this dream, they fell asleep again, and soon the day came.

They approached the magnificent gate. "Let's open it, Enkidu! Let's be on our way!"

For a last time, Enkidu tried to persuade his friend to turn back.

But since the King would not listen, it was he who went first and placed his hand against the gate to push it open. Enkidu was thrown backward with such violence that he fell to the earth. He rose to his feet. "Gilgamesh, wait! My hand is paralyzed!"

"Put it on my arm, Enkidu! It will take strength from my arm because I am not afraid."

When the two friends threw their weight against the gate, however, it swung inward.

They walked up the mountainside through the sacred trees. And these became closer and thicker until the sky was blotted out. They could hear the giant heartbeat of Humbaba and smell the smoke from his lungs.

To show his daring, Gilgamesh cut one of the cedar trees. The blows of his axe rang out, and from afar the terrible Humbaba heard the sound.

With a crashing of timbers and a rolling of loose stones, Humbaba came down upon them. His face loomed among the tree tops, creased and grooved like some ancient rock. The breath he breathed withered the boughs of cedar and set small fires everywhere.

Enkidu's fears now vanished and the two heroes stood side by side as the monster advanced. He loomed over them, his arms swinging out like the masts of a ship. He was almost upon them when suddenly the friends stepped apart. The giant demon lurched through the trees, stumbled, and fell flat. He rose to his feet bellowing like a bull and charged upon Enkidu. But the King brought down his axe on the toe of Humbaba so that he whirled about roaring with pain. He grasped Gilgamesh by his flowing hair, swung him round and round as if to hurl him through the treetops, but now Enkidu saw his giant ribs exposed and he thrust his sword into the monster's side. Liquid fire gushed from the wound and ran in small streams down the mountainside. Gilgamesh fell to the earth and lay still, trying to breathe. But meanwhile Humbaba grasped the horns of Enkidu and began to flail his body against a tree. Surely the wild man would have died, but now Gilgamesh roused himself. He lanced into the air his long spear with its handle of lapis lazuli and gold. The spear caught Humbaba in the throat and remained there poised and glittering among the fires that had ignited everywhere.

The giant loosened his hold on Enkidu; he cried out. The earth reverberated with the sound, and distant mountains shook.

Gilgamesh felt pity in his heart. He withdrew his sword and put down his axe, while the monster Humbaba crept toward him grovelling and wailing for help. Now Enkidu perceived that the monster drew in a long breath in order to spew forth his last weapon—the searing fire that would consume the King. He leaped on the demon and with many sword thrusts released the fire, so that it bubbled harmlessly among the stones.

Humbaba was dead; the two heroes, black with soot and dirt, were still alive. They hugged each other; they leaped about; and singing and shouting, they descended the mountainside. Gentle rains fell around them and the land was forever free from the curse of the giant Humbaba.

The Wooing of Ishtar

As the two friends fought with Humbaba, the goddess Ishtar heard the tumult and descended from the sky onto the mountain. What mortal dared to challenge the servant of the gods? Who would dare to invade the cedar forest?

Ishtar prepared to call together the gods for a battle. But first she stood for a while to watch the terrible fracas. As she watched, she began to admire the two heroes, their agility and their courage. Thus standing quietly, she saw the destruction of Humbaba. And at the same time she fell in love with Gilgamesh.

She followed the two warriors down the mountainside, heard their laughter, listened to their boasts while they bathed in a fresh spring and put on clean garments. She hid in a clump of bushes and watched over them while they slept through a night and half a day. Then she called to Gilgamesh: "O King of the city, I have watched your battle with my servant Humbaba. I have seen the desecration of my forest. Terrible will be your reckoning when the gods learn of this insolence!"

Gilgamesh jumped to his feet and looked all around him. "Enkidu, am I dreaming again? Did I hear a voice? Did I hear threats against us?"

"I too heard them, O King."

"But wait," Ishtar continued, "I am prepared to forgive you, Gilgamesh. I will take you as my husband and set you among the stars. I will petition the gods to forgive you. As the husband of Ishtar, you will be above reproach."

"Save your threats, great Ishtar," Gilgamesh called out. "I am not afraid. We two, Enkidu and I, have done a good thing. We have saved the bright face of Shamash; we have rid the city of the demon that daily threatened it with smoke and fire; we have delivered the shepherds and the farmers from the monster that each year devoured their huts and their flocks, and that cast its blight over their fields of grain! We have freed the people from terror, O Ishtar, we have earned honor for ourselves and our name will be great among mankind. We need no favors!"

At this, Ishtar wept, and her tears were like liquid starlight as they ran down her cheeks and splashed on the ground. "O Gilgamesh, your chariot will be of gold, and its wheels will be made of carnelian!"

"I need no chariot, O Ishtar! My friend and I will be carried on the shoulders of young men! The children of Uruk will scatter flowers before us!"

"As my husband, Gilgamesh, kings will bow down before you. Your goats will bear triplets, your sheep twins. Your oxen will have no rival for strength, your horses no equal in running!"

"Poets will sing of our deeds, O Goddess, old men will praise us! We will be kissed by all the girls in Uruk!"

"Beware your arrogance, Gilgamesh! The goddess Ishtar does not offer her love lightly!"

"I know about your love, mighty Ishtar. Whomever you love, you soon tire of and destroy:

> There was beautiful Tammuz, your husband,
> Him you consigned to Hell for one-half of each year!
> There was the sweet-singing bird, the Rollo that loved you,
> But you broke his wing and cracked his voice
> So that he flutters around croaking, '*kappi*, *kappi*!'
> There was the fleet, free horse that you loved,
> Your gift to him was the spur, the whip, the bit!
> There was the proud, unconquerable lion; you admired him,
> For him you dug a pit and set a trap!
> The shepherd of the herd adored you,
> You turned him into a wolf
> So that his own sons drive him away
> And his own dogs bite at his shanks!
> Your father's palm gardener loved you,
> You turned him into a mole
> That must burrow under the earth this way and that
> And never again will see the sun that he loves!
> If I loved you, Ishtar, you would destroy me too!

Such was the reply of Gilgamesh to the goddess.

Ishtar shrieked with such violence that it seemed as though the sky would split apart; then she ascended into the heavens. With loud cries she summoned together all the gods from the places where they were, in order to rouse them against the King.

But Gilgamesh and Enkidu, careless and gay, turned their faces toward Uruk.

The city had never before and has never since witnessed such a celebration as that which greeted the adventurers on their return from the battle with Humbaba. A holiday was declared. All work ceased. Feasts were laid out everywhere, and the people went up and down the streets carrying standards and bright banners. The young and the old gathered in the family house and sat cross-legged while the two heroes told the story repeating it again and again and answering all the questions that were asked. Singers immediately made up long songs about the adventure; dancers acted it out; and scribes laboriously engraved it on stone, or pressed the words and letters into tablets of wet clay. Runners carried the clay tablets from city to city and when it was asked, "Who is this Gilgamesh?", the answer was given:

He who has seen everything,
He who knows everything,
He stands seven cubits high;
Two-thirds of him is god,
One-third of him is man;
He is the most glorious among heroes,
He is the most eminent among men,
And Enkidu is his companion!

Such was the return of the two heroes to Uruk-of-the-Walls. Gilgamesh went to the palace of his mother who welcomed him with the greatest joy. Enkidu, on the other hand, hurried to the temple of Ishtar to look for gentle Harim. But there he found the courtyards empty, the doors shut, the gates bolted.

The Bull of Heaven

As the gods gathered together from all the places where they were, Ishtar told them about the desecration of the cedar forest and the killing of Humbaba by the mortals, Gilgamesh and Enkidu. And her greatest fury was toward Gilgamesh because of his insult to her and his rejection of her love.

"O Father Anu, I will have vengeance and you must help me!"

"What is your plan, Ishtar?" asked her brother Enlil, god of the earth and the affairs of men.

"Father Anu will create the Bull of Heaven. The Bull will then descend to the earth, to the city of Uruk; it will demolish everything; it will trample all the people; it will kill Gilgamesh!"

"I will do nothing of the sort!" said Anu. "Ishtar, my daughter, you have asked for this insult. Why does it upset you so much to have your evil deeds laid out before you by a brave man?"

"I will have my vengeance, Father!" Ishtar's fury increased.

Shamash now opened his mouth and spoke: "Great Anu, powerful Enlil, Ea of the deep waters, hear me! It was I who sought the destruction of Humbaba. It was I who planted the idea in the brave heart of Gilgamesh. For each year, after all my toil in ripening the grain, Humbaba destroyed it; he burned it. To the mortal people whom I love, Humbaba was an enemy; he destroyed their houses; he filled the skies with smoke and soot and dark clouds, concealing my face. Who else could have destroyed the monster but Gilgamesh and his noble companion?"

The god Enlil roared out with rage, and with his breath the seven winds tore about this way and that. "O Shamash! Seeing that you go out each day to shed your light on the human race, why don't you go down and join them? Are you a god or a mortal? Why should you turn on us to protect and help them?"

Ishtar's voice rose to a shriek: "Father Anu, create the Bull of Heaven! Otherwise I will smash down the doors of the underworld. I will let them stand open so that the dead will rise up and join the living! They will be more numerous; they will eat up all the food of the living so that there will be famine on the earth!"

The gods turned away their faces in dread, and Anu created the Bull of Heaven.

The Bull roared through the gates of Uruk, smashing them as though they had been made of straw. Hearing the clamor, a hundred workmen rushed out to defend the city, and the Bull mowed them down, trampling them. Two hundred men met him with staves and with clubs. These he gored pitilessly and tossed them aside. He surged onward through the streets, past temples,

through gardens and groves of trees, uprooting them as he went. Women screamed and hid in dark corners, clasping their children to them.

Three hundred warriors now came out with spears and swords to meet the awful beast, and Enkidu too heard the uproar. He saw the lightning flashes that were struck from the pavement by the Bull's bronze hooves, and he rushed to join the fighters. Seeing him, the Bull rose and plunged toward him and sought to gore him, and Enkidu met all this with his own mighty horns. For a time he held the creature back, but lightning surrounded them and he fell. Then he saw the bright spear of Gilgamesh, the spear with the handle of gold and lapis lazuli. It sped through the air and struck the beast in its throat and remained there, poised and glittering.

Again the two friends stood together and fought side by side. The Bull seemed indestructible and for hours the battle raged. The people watched and whispered, "What mortal men could prevail against such a beast as this?" But now Gilgamesh danced before the animal luring it with his tunic and his bright weapons. Enkidu thrust his sword deep between the nape of the neck and the horns and killed it.

A wail of anguish split the air. Looking upward, the heroes saw the goddess Ishtar crouched upon the high wall above the city. She uttered a curse upon them: "Woe to Gilgamesh who has dishonored my name! Woe to Enkidu who has killed the Bull of Heaven!"

In his wrath, Enkidu wrenched off the right leg of the beast up to the thigh. He hurled it to the top of the wall, where it lay before the goddess. "May you receive this offering in your face, O terrible Ishtar!"

There was quiet in the town, and mourning. Gilgamesh called together the artisans and the tradesmen, and he divided the carcass of the Bull among them. To the butchers he gave the meat, to the bronze workers, the hooves. To the jewelers and the craftsmen in stone, he gave the great horns that were made of lapis lazuli and weighed two talents each. To the furriers he gave its pelt and to the ivory workers its teeth; for every part of the marvelous animal had been made of some precious stone or other rich material.

As to the entrails of the Bull, these he put into a pot, and seasoning them with the most fragrant of herbs and spices, he set them over an altar fire so that the pleasant odors might reach the region that the gods inhabit. "O great Shamash, accept my prayers of gratitude, my thanks for your protection, for otherwise my friend and I would surely have been killed."

The Vengeance of Ishtar

In the night, Enkidu jumped up from his couch and called his friend, "O Gilgamesh, my dreams are full of threats and omens!"

"Tell me what they're about. I'll consult with Ninsun!"

"I was standing by the wall of the city. I looked upward toward the top of the wall and there, crouching like some dark bird, was the goddess, Ishtar. All the priestesses, Harim too, were gathered around her and the temple yard was empty. They set up a howl, a lamentation over the leg of the Bull that I, Enkidu, yesterday threw at the goddess—

"I was not afraid," Enkidu went on, "but then the gods, hearing the awful noise, gathered around her and they were angry. Anu opened his mouth and spoke—even Father Anu, and he said, 'They have entered the cedar gate; they have desecrated the forest; they have killed Humbaba, guardian of the wild cows, and our servant; they have insulted the goddess Ishtar; they have killed the Bull of Heaven; and one of them shall die!'

"He asked the gods to decide which one of us should die and Enlil answered, 'Enkidu shall die!'

"The god Shamash of the bright face came forward and argued for me saying, 'Why should Enkidu be the one?' But Enlil ridiculed him and told him to go down to earth and live with mankind. And the gods agreed that I should die."

Tears came to the eyes of Gilgamesh. "O my friend, my younger brother, why should the gods acquit me and not you? Haven't we done all things together? Go to sleep, Enkidu!"

But Enkidu grew feverish and his dreams increased.

Gilgamesh sat beside him. "Listen, Enkidu, I would not let them take you. If they took you, I would sit by the gate of the underworld and never move until they released you and brought you back!"

Enkidu became ill; in his dreams he saw the tall cedar gate. He spoke to it as though it had been some living thing: "Because I admired your beauty, I didn't destroy you; I didn't cut you down, but if I had known what evil you concealed, I would have hacked you to pieces!"

Next he dreamed of his days as a wild man and he called for his friends, the gazelle and the little wild horse, the foxes and the rabbits. Bitterly, he cursed the hunter: "May your traps remain forever empty! May the wild creatures that you hunt turn on you and pursue you!"

Worst of all were his curses against Harim: "O Priestess, it was you who trapped me in the forest! It was you who lured me to the hut of the shepherd; it was you who led me into the streets of the city! May those streets be your only dwelling place forever! May you crouch in the shade of the wall! May the rain and the wind be your garments, and dry crusts your only food! May your only companions be the low, the drunken, and the outcast!"

The god Shamash heard the terrible curses of Enkidu and he called down to him out of the sky: "Enkidu, my son! Wake up! Why should you curse the hunter? Why should you revile the dear priestess who loves you faithfully? Who was it, Enkidu, that first taught you to speak? Who was it that tore her own garment to make you a tunic? Who taught you to eat bread and to drink wine fit for the gods? Who brought you before the King when he welcomed you as his brother, so that you became a hero and so that the princes of the earth knelt before you to kiss your feet?"

Enkidu wakened and he called out for the vanished priestess: "O Harim, dear Harim, may you be forever favored by the gods! May you reign forever young and beautiful! May kings open their storehouses and spread their treasures before you! May you be forever admired, forever loved, forever envied—whether by the young girls or the mothers of seven! May every heart yearn for you!"

Other dreams afflicted Enkidu; he dreamed of a palace in which kings and princes were only servants. They waited on the gods; they bathed them; they carried out orders with many bows; they served wine to the gods and brought them baked goods.

Then he dreamed of the Zu bird that attacked him with sharp talons.

For twelve days and twelve nights Enkidu lay on his couch, his friend sitting beside him. On the thirteenth day he turned over and lay like a worm, on his face.

Gilgamesh spoke to him; he called him: "Enkidu, Enkidu, what sleep has taken hold of you? You are dark! Your ears don't listen to me! Your eyes look at me and they are no different from the clay! Enkidu, remember how we have wrestled with panthers? Remember how we have run fast alongside the little wild horses on the steppes? Remember how the people greeted us, Enkidu! Remember how they embraced us and sang songs about us?" Gilgamesh walked back and forth beside his friend; he grieved; he tore out his hair.

He ordered the artisans to make two bowls, one of carnelian stone and one of lapis lazuli. The first, he filled with honey, the second with butter. He set them on a table made of elammqu—the scented sandalwood. He put them into the sunlight during the brightest part of the day. Then he took them to his friend's couch and set them beside him. "O Enkidu, here is food full of the life-giving light of Shamash, the sun. Eat it, Enkidu; it will bring the life back into your body." But Enkidu lay still.

Gilgamesh then ordered the elders of Uruk to have made for his friend a couch of gold. He ordered that robes of finest cloth and embroidery be made for Enkidu, and that he be dressed in them and treated as a king.

But Gilgamesh threw off his own rich clothing. He dressed himself in the pelts of wild animals and threw away all his gay trappings and ornaments.

In the night he went to his mother's bedside. "O Ninsun, what fate has overtaken my friend, Enkidu? He didn't die in battle; no disease attacked him; he did not die of venerable old age. The earth reached up and seized him. Mother, will I too die? Will I too turn into clay?"

"In time, dear Gilgamesh, all people die."

"Even I, Mother, who am two-parts god?"

"One part of you is man, O Gilgamesh!"

"Tell me, Ninsun, about my ancestor, Utnapishtim. I have heard that he is one that lives forever and does not die!"

"So they say," Ninsun replied, "but who knows about Utnapishtim—"

"I'll find him! I'll learn from him the secret of life and death!"

Tears fell from the eyes of pale Ninsun. "Utnapishtim, your ancestor, lives somewhere beyond the Bitter River. Thus, he is called Utnapishtim the Distant. You know well, Gilgamesh, that no one who is alive can cross that river; it is death itself. Stay here, my son!"

But he only cried out, "I will find him! I will find him!"

As the first shimmer of dawn appeared, Gilgamesh set out from the city of Uruk.

PART TWO

The Wanderings of Gilgamesh

The Scorpion Men

It is not known how many double-hours, that is, how many days and nights Gilgamesh walked. But he crossed deserts and rocky places and came in time to the edge of the world. Before him loomed the mighty mountains of Mashu, and he asked himself, "Can these be the mountains whose peaks reach into the heavens, and whose feet reach below the bottom of the earth? Is this the bank of the sun—the edge between day and night? Is this the mountain guarded by the terrible scorpion men whose radiance blinds one and whose look is death?"

And as he stood questioning himself, he looked upward and saw these men standing above him in the snowy pass; and they sparkled and shone with a bright radiance.

He heard one of the creatures call out to his wife, "Who is this that comes here, is he god or man?"

The wife called back, "Two-thirds of his flesh is the same as that of the gods, but the other third is a man's flesh."

The scorpion man called down to him, cupping his hands, "How is it that you've come here to me, crossing deserts and all sorts of difficult places?"

Gilgamesh shouted back despairingly, "O, I have lost my friend, Enkidu, sir, he who roved the fields and woods with me and was my constant companion. The earth reached up and seized him!"

"But why do you come here to this place?"

"I have come to search for Utnapishtim, my ancestor. He was once a mortal man, but he entered the assembly of the gods. He knows the secret of life and death; I must find out from him where my friend has gone and whether I too must die!"

"O Gilgamesh," said the scorpion man, "no one has ever done this thing. Deep are the caverns that lie under the mountain, those very caverns that the sun travels on his way back to the Eastern Garden.

"At a distance of nine double-hours only, Gilgamesh, the heart fails. Dense is the darkness; there is no light! At a distance of ten double-hours, the mind fails! At first, the cold is unbearable, but in the middle part, the heat is unbearable. And although the whole distance is only that of twelve double-hours, it is the same distance as that between life and death! Turn back, Gilgamesh!"

But Gilgamesh replied, "Even if my heart fails, I will go on! In heat or cold I will go on. Sighing or weeping I will go on!"

The scorpion man was silent for a time, but when he spoke he said, "Go, Gilgamesh! I will open the gates for you. May your feet carry you in safety!"

As the gates of rock swung open Gilgamesh entered into the earth and followed the way of the sun. Darkness closed around him; he could not see what lay ahead of him or what way he had come. The path was strewn with rocks and he stumbled often. At first, his body shook with cold, but as he descended more and more deeply into the earth, heat surrounded him, and he sweat and panted for breath. Sometimes he seemed to have been walking only a short way, but at other times he felt that he had been trudging his life out in the darkness. There was no sound there other than the unceasing scraping of his own feet as he felt his way along.

He strained his eyes to see, but it was as though they were closed. There was nothing, no trace of light. Could the caverns be endless? Had the scorpion man only trapped him, and was he now laughing at him, high up in the mountain pass?

At a distance of nine double-hours, Gilgamesh's heart failed him and he was full of terror. At a distance of ten double-hours his mind failed him. He opened his mouth and shouted with all his might and the echoes of his own voice swarmed back all around him, terrible to hear. He began to run, but he stumbled and fell.

So Gilgamesh lay in the darkness and could no longer cry out. He closed his eyes; he could not get up or turn backward or go forward. And then he felt the wind from the north blowing upon his face.

He rose and stumbled on in the black place. At a distance of eleven double-hours he perceived a trace of light and his eyes filled with tears of joy. At a distance of twelve double-hours he emerged from the cavern and stood in the Eastern Garden.

All around him rose trees that sparkled with precious gems. Water glittered in fountains and in pools; the air was full of sweet smells, and flowers of every kind nodded in the breeze. Here was such a light as he had never seen. "Can this be the Eastern Garden,

called Dilmun, the most beautiful of places?" As Gilgamesh wondered, he looked through the trees into the huge face of Shamash, the sun.

Shamash came to him, greeting him, and Gilgamesh called out to him, "O great Shamash, the darkness has gone from my eyes! Let me only gaze at you! Let me look at you and be filled with your light!"

"What are you doing here, my son?" asked Shamash. "How have you come here? Why are you dressed in the rough skins of animals? Why are your looks so wild, your face burned, your body so thin and emaciated?"

"I have lost my friend and brother Enkidu! The earth came up and seized him and since that time I have known no rest. Now, O great Shamash, I am on my way to find my ancestor who was chosen a long time ago to live among the immortals. From him I shall learn the secret of life and death; I will preserve life!"

"Why do you run hither and thither, Gilgamesh? The life you seek you will never find!"

"Tell me," said Gilgamesh, "shall the one who has died rest his head forever underneath the earth? Shall he sleep for all the years and never see your light, O Shamash? And shall I too die?"

"Why should you waste your young years this way, my son? Stay here beside me! Live in this garden where there is no grief and no memory!"

But Gilgamesh would not rest or remain in the garden. "In your travels across the sky, great Shamash, you must see all things! Tell me then how to find my ancestor in the place of the immortals."

Shamash pointed to a path that led downward through the jeweled trees. "In that direction you will find Sabitu, the wine maiden. She will tell you the way to go. But remember, Gilgamesh, what you seek has never been." And so speaking, Shamash gathered his glorious robes about him and ascended into the sky.

Sabitu

The maiden, Sabitu was in front of her house tending her casks of wine. Hearing footsteps, she looked up and saw the wild countenance of Gilgamesh. She ran into her house and bolted the door. "Surely some murderer has made his way here—some savage!"

But Gilgamesh knocked and pleaded with her to open her door. "I am Gilgamesh, King of distant Uruk! Talk to me, O Sabitu, tell me what I want to know!"

Sabitu was overcome by curiosity. "If you are a king, why are you dressed in the skins of wild animals? Why is your face burned as though you had walked through a furnace? Why are you wan and unkempt like a wild man?"

When Gilgamesh told her of his grief and his fearful journey beneath the earth, the maiden was moved by pity. She came out of her house and invited him to sit on a bench beside her. She brought him wine and meat and fruits and comforted him with kind words.

"But where are you going, Gilgamesh?"

"I am on my way to find my ancester, Utnapishtim. He lives somewhere among the immortals; from him I shall learn the secret of life and death!"

"Ah, whither do you run, Gilgamesh? The life you seek you will never find!"

"Only tell me the path, Sabitu. If it is a sea that I must cross, then I will cross it, but if not, then I will walk over the desert and the wild steppes, but still I will find Utnapishtim!"

"Deep are the waters, Gilgamesh! Whoever has come even so far as this place has never yet made the crossing. For ahead of you now lies the Bitter River whose waters are death. When you come to the edge of the water, what will you do?"

And she went on, saying, "Listen to me Gilgamesh; when the gods created mankind they allotted death to mankind, but life they retained in their own keeping! Rest here, O King! Let your garments be clean and your headband made of gold! Be glad; let your belly be full! Drink the good sesame wine and make every day a day of rejoicing! Take a wife to your bosom; such is the life the gods allotted to mankind!"

Gilgamesh thanked her. "I must go on, O Sabitu. Tell me which way I must take."

Sabitu led Gilgamesh by his hand to the edge of her garden. She pointed toward a vast plain of dark and dismal water, edged by a white shore. "That way, O King, lies the Bitter River. On the shore you will find an ancient boat and the pilot, Urshanabi. Only he can take you across, but no living man has ever sat beside him!" She wished him well and returned to her vineyard.

How Gilgamesh Crossed the Bitter River

Thus Gilgamesh came to the Bitter River. He looked out across its water and up and down the shore, but nowhere could he see either boat or boatman. He walked farther and after some distance he espied a boat and went to it. Still there was no person nearby. He called; he cupped his hands and shouted but there was no answer. He sat down beside the boat and waited—he could not tell how long, for there was neither day nor night by which to measure the time. He was impatient; he searched; he called continually and there was no reply.

Raging, Gilgamesh picked up a huge rock and with it he smashed

the stone oarlocks of the boat. Indeed, he might have destroyed the boat itself, but he heard a voice shouting at him: "Hello, there! What are you doing? Who are you who dares to lay hands on the boat of Utnapishtim?"

Utnapishtim! Gilgamesh cursed his impatience and his rage. "O I am weary, boatman! I have come far. I have crossed the Mountains of Mashu and walked under the foundation of the earth! In heat and cold I have come! Sighing and weeping I have come ever onward to seek my ancestor, Utnapishtim! Forgive my rage, O boatman; forgive my anger, for I've grown impatient. Only take me across this water to the place of Utnapishtim!"

The boatman shook his head. "No living being has ever crossed these waters, young man. But even if I were willing to ferry you over, it's you who have made that impossible for you have destroyed the oarlocks of the boat."

Gilgamesh felt shame and bowed his head. Then the boatman spoke softly, "Broad is the water, O Wanderer, but if it is your will to cross then you must do as I say: you must enter the forest and there you must cut and hew one hundred and ten straight poles, measuring sixty cubits each. With these we will pole our way across the river. Each pole, once it has reached its length, must be thrown away, for if even so much as a drop of water enters the boat or touches your flesh, you will die."

Urshanabi, the boatman then lay down on the beach to sleep while Gilgamesh went into the forest to cut the poles. And when this labor was finished he pulled them to the boat and laid them along its length. And all this done, they set out across the width of the Bitter River.

Utnapishtim

Utnapishtim is lying in his hammock before the door of his house. He calls to his wife saying, "I see the boat approaching across the water, but the boatman is not alone; someone is with him. Come and tell me who it is that rides in the boat with Urshanabi!"

His wife comes out of the house and shades her eyes, looking across the water. "It is a young man not different from you and me, but his body is thin and his looks are wan!"

The boat comes to rest beside the quay and Gilgamesh leaps out and approaches Utnapishtim, his ancestor. He falls to his knees and looks at him. "O Utnapishtim, I gaze upon you and your face is not different from mine! I had thought to find you a dreadful warrior, towering and tall, but here you are lying on your side in your hammock like any mortal man!"

"I am not like you at all!" shouts Utnapishtim. "Look at you, unkempt and woebegone, and dressed in the filthy hides of wild animals! Who are you and how did you get here?"

"I am Gilgamesh, King of Uruk, O Utnapishtim, and you are my ancestor. I have come far, through deserts and over wild steppes and under the very foundation of the earth to find you and to ask you a question . . ."

"You have no right to come here, you a mortal man. The boatman shall be punished!"

"Listen to me, O Utnapishtim! I had a friend dearer to me than a brother. Day and night we went together; together we roamed over the wild steppes and through the forests, hunting and wrestling with wild animals. Together we demolished the monster Humbaba that daily threatened our city; together we killed the Bull of Heaven that had been sent against us to destroy us. Everywhere we walked together, sharing all dangers and all delights. Then death came to Enkidu: the fate of mortal men overtook him! He did not die in battle like some hero; he didn't die of illness or venerable old age; the earth came up and seized him! Then, O Utnapishtim, I was overcome by terror and by grief. Alone, I set out over the wild places of the earth to find you, my ancestor. For I have been told that you were chosen to join the assembly of the gods, and that you know the secret of life and death. Tell me now, O Utnapishtim, must my brother remain for all the years lying at the center of the earth? Will he never again see the face of the sun, and must I too die?"

Utnapishtim speaks, answering Gilgamesh, "Do we build a house to last forever? Do brothers share their inheritance to last forever? When the gods gather together, O Gilgamesh, they decree the destinies of men. The days of life they measure out, but the days of death they do not measure!"

"Then tell me, Utnapishtim, what secret do you know? In what way did you come to be placed among the immortals? Were you, like me, two-parts god and only one-part mortal man?"

"Not at all," says Utnapishtim. "Squat down on your haunches Gilgamesh and listen. I will tell you the story; I will reveal to you the secret of my immortality!"

The Secret of Utnapishtim

"It was many many years ago," he begins. "I lived in a place called Shuruppak, a city already old and full of vices. Now the people of this place thought of nothing but pleasure and they spent all their time talking, arguing, shouting, and singing!

"Carrying on like this they raised a commotion, a loud noise, and this noise rose to heaven and it disturbed the gods, particularly the god Enlil.

"Enlil called together an assembly of the gods and he complained, 'They are making too much noise down there; I don't like it; I cannot sleep!' When the gods asked him what he proposed to do about it he said, 'I have conceived a plan whereby I can destroy all the people on earth and thus get some rest. In fact,' the god said, 'I have arranged a hurricane that will wipe out mankind, a deluge that will drown every living thing!'

"The gods disagreed, and they quarreled. Some wished only to punish mankind. Others said, 'We could send down a plague that would diminish the numbers of people on earth.' But Enlil is powerful and his domain is earth itself. He said to them, 'I reveal my plan to you the gods, but not one of you is to speak a word of it to any mortal man. No one is to survive!'

"In truth, Gilgamesh, no god spoke to me or told me anything. Yet one night I heard a voice and it seemed much like the voice of my lord, Ea. The voice came close to the wall of my house and spoke to it, saying:

'Reed hut, reed hut!
Wall, wall!
Reed hut, listen!
Wall, hear!
Let the man of Shuruppak, son of Ubar-tatu
Tear down his house,
Destroy all,
Abandon everything!
Let him build a ship
To save life, to escape the storm,
Let him take onto the ship,
Seed of every living thing,
Of creeping things and flying things,
Domestic creatures and wild beasts,
And all those creatures that eat grass,
His wife, and his daughter. . . . '

"So I, as a carpenter, was given the dimensions of the ship, the height, the width, and the breadth. And, speaking beside the wall of my house, I asked, 'But what shall I say to the people of Shuruppak?'

'Say to them,' the voice went on,
' "The god Enlil is displeased with me,
Therefore I go to dwell upon the waters
That are the domain of my lord, Ea.
But as for you, the people of Shuruppak,
A rain of wealth will fall upon you,
Rain of barley,
Rain of birds and of fishes,
Rain of harvest wealth!" '

"Then," Utnapishtim goes on, "I laid the keel and constructed the framework according to the measurements. I directed the laborers and the artisans, and even children carried baskets of pitch. To keep the workmen happy I killed bullocks from the herd, and I poured out red wine and white wine like water. We put the covering over her; I loaded the ship; I dismissed the builders."

"And what became of all the people of Shuruppak?"

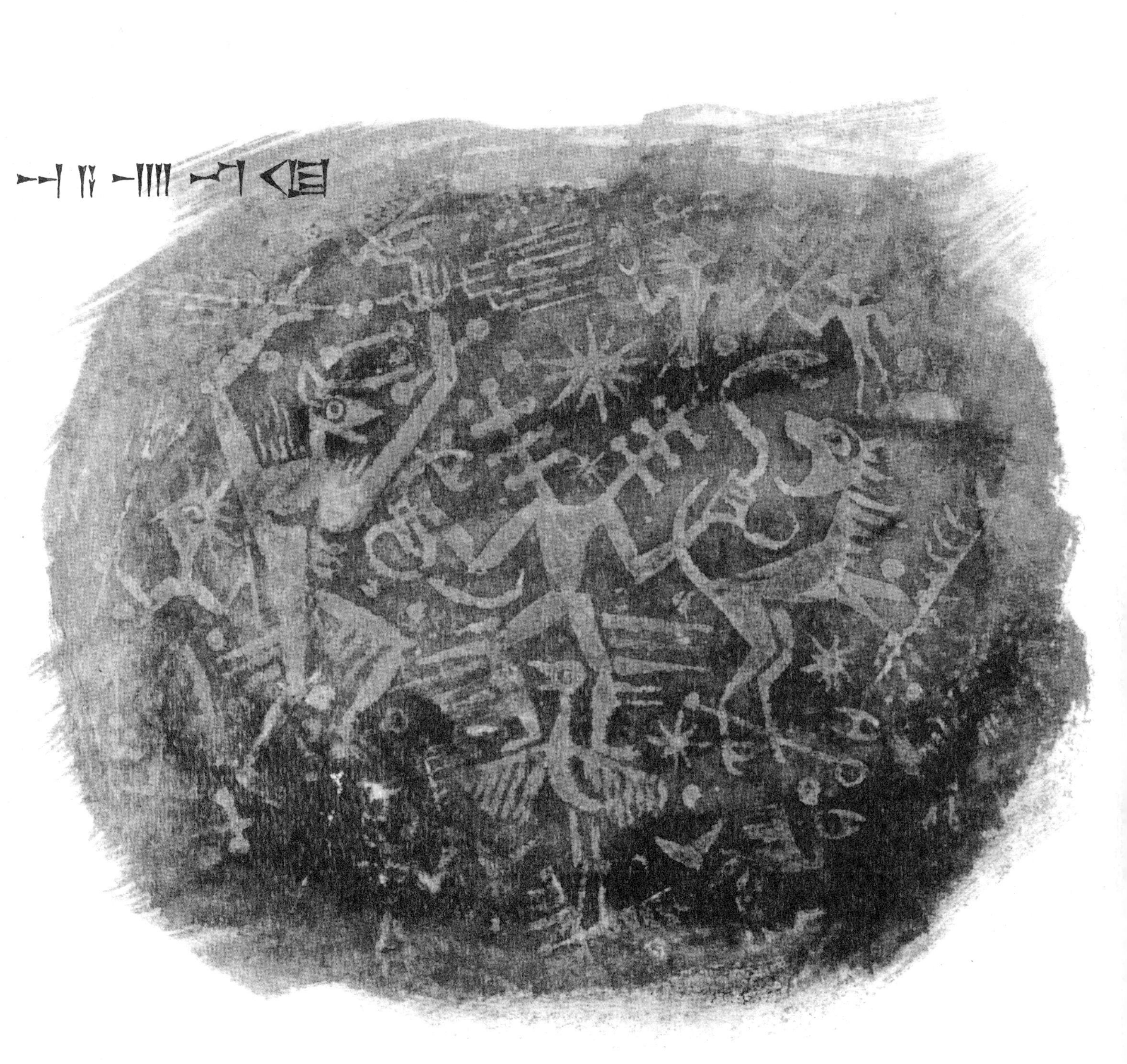

"The tempest came over the people like a battle! No man could see his neighbor. Adad thundered, and the demons of the wind ran this way and that. The Anunnaki waved their torches of lightning; then darkness came and water roared over the land. All that had been light became blackness; the dikes gave way and the earth was broken in pieces like a pot.

"For six days and six nights the storm blew. The gods were terrified and they huddled together like dogs. Great Ishtar wept. She wrung her hands, saying to Enlil, 'O why did I not oppose you in the assembly of the gods! How could I agree to such evil! How could I allow the destruction of my people, my children who now lie like dead fish in the sea?'

"When the seventh day came the storm abated. I opened a window and looked around me and everywhere there was water; there was no land to be seen. Everything was silence and all mankind was turned to clay!

"As I stood there weeping," Utnapishtim continues, "the top of a mountain took hold of the bottom of the ship and held it fast. I saw the water begin to recede so I let a dove go free. It flew round and round, but it came back for there was no place where it could alight. After some time I sent out a swallow; it too returned, but there was mud on its feet. I sent out a crow and she flew this way and that; she found food, she ate, she cawed; she flew away and did not return!

"When the top of the mountain lifted up out of the water, I left the ship and stood on the earth. And in my gratitude I poured wine onto the mountain-top.

"I set up seven kettles that I might make a feast for the gods. Under these kettles I made fires of fragrant cedar, cane and myrtle; and I filled them with meat which I had seasoned with herbs. The gods smelled the odor; they smelled the sweet odor, and they gathered like flies around the cooking-pots.

"Ishtar came, wearing her necklace of gold and gems. 'O great gods,' she cried out, 'as I shall never forget my jewels, so will I never forget these days of destruction! Let all the gods join the feast, but not Enlil who brought on the flood!'

"Enlil, however, saw my ship and he drew near. His anger was terrible to see. He accused all the gods in turn, saying, 'Has any mortal escaped? No one was to live through the destruction!'

"The gods pointed to Ea, and he answered in this way: 'O Enlil, how could you willfully do this thing? You might have punished those who did wrong; you might have sent wolves or lions against those who offended you; you might have wiped out some of the people; but why should you want to destroy mankind? Even so, Enlil, I did not reveal your secret to any living man!'

"Enlil came toward us. He took my wife and me by the hand and led us onto the ship. He made us kneel. He touched our foreheads. 'Hitherto,' he said, 'Utnapishtim has been a man. Now

he and his wife shall be like unto us gods. He shall be immortal; he shall dwell at a distance, at the confluence of the rivers . . .'

"So you see," Utnapishtim tells Gilgamesh, "it was a god that interceded for me. But who will intercede for you, O Gilgamesh? Who will call together a meeting of the gods for you? Who will grant you the life you seek?"

Gilgamesh, wan and weary after all his hardships, has fallen asleep. Utnapishtim wakens him. "Don't you know that the immortals never sleep, O King Gilgamesh! Come, let me see you stay awake for seven days and seven nights!"

Gilgamesh agrees, but soon his head nods.

Utnapishtim turns to his wife. "See how the strong man sits on his hams! Sleep, like a rainstorm blows over him!"

But the wife pities the young man. "Waken him, husband! Let him go back along the way by which he came!"

"Remember, O wife, how deceitful are the ways of mortals! I must prove to this one that he is not fit to dwell among us." Utnapishtim then orders his wife to bake a fresh loaf of bread for each day during which Gilgamesh sleeps, and to place each loaf at his head.

Seven days have passed and Utnapishtim rouses Gilgamesh who says, "I had hardly nodded, O carpenter, when you touched my arm!"

"Then count your loaves, young man; a fresh one has been baked for each day during which you slept."

Gilgamesh counts the loaves and the first is fresh and still warm, but the second is cold. The third is already stale and the fourth hard. The fifth is cracked and dry, the sixth black, and the seventh has begun to mold.

Such is the greeting of Utnapishtim toward Gilgamesh who traveled far and suffered hardships only to see him.

The Magic Weed

When he looked at the loaves of bread Gilgamesh was desolate. "O Utnapishtim, where shall I go now? Whither shall my steps lead me? Numbness grasps at my limbs; the earth holds my feet!"

But Utnapishtim spoke only to the boatman: "Take him to the washing-place! Let him throw off the animal skins that hide his fine figure. Give him a fresh tunic and a gold band for his head so that he may be dressed suitably for a king. Then, I will grant him a favor; I will decree that his garment shall remain fresh and not be soiled for all the days of his journey home!"

"But as for you, Urshanabi, you have betrayed us: you have disgraced the crossing and the landing-place. May you never be seen here again! May the quay hate you; may the shore turn you away!"

Urshanabi took Gilgamesh to the washing-place, as he was told. He repaired the ferry-boat. He entered it, and with Gilgamesh beside him, pushed off from the shore.

The wife of Utnapishtim scolded him thus: "O husband, the young man has suffered all sorts of pain and hardship only to see you and talk to you. How can you send him off like this? What will you give him from this place so that he may return to his city in honor?"

Utnapishtim called the boat back to the quay. "Gilgamesh, I will tell you something, namely, a secret of the gods. At the bottom of this river there grows a weed. It bears a flower having the fragrance of a rose. Like a rose too, it has a thorny stem that will prick and scratch the hands. Nevertheless, if any mortal can grasp this weed, if he can pluck it and eat some morsel of it, youth will return to him as the spring-time returns to the year! This secret I tell you."

Gilgamesh shouted loud with joy; "Urshanabi, we shall grasp the weed and pull it loose! We will return to Uruk, you and I; we will share the weed among the aged of the city and they will regain their youth and strength. We will call it 'The-Old-Become-Young-Again!' "

"Beware, O Gilgamesh! This is a trap for your wayward heart! The waters of the river are death, and no one may enter them and still live."

"Old men will become strong again! Grandmothers will become maids!"

"Instead, you will be overcome by the bitter water, O King. Come, let the weed stay where it grows!"

"But if I can grasp the weed it will restore my strength and I will live. Take the boat out on the water, Urshanabi, and wait for me."

Gilgamesh stood on the quay and tied heavy stones to his feet. Slowly he entered the river and the stones pulled him down. The water was thick and full of brine and he could not see. But such was the fragrance of the flower that it penetrated everywhere. Gilgamesh was drawn to it; he touched it; he pulled it out by its roots even though it pricked and scratched his hands. He cut the stones from his feet and the water rejected him and threw him to the far shore.

There Urshanabi waited and they set out across the land and walked for an unknown distance. They crossed mountains; they came to the sacred forest and passed through it and reached the twilight.

They sat down to rest and tempted by curiosity, they tasted a morsel of the plant. Immediately all weariness dropped from them. "Let's go on," they said to each other. And now, guided by the rising and sinking of the sun, they walked a distance of twenty double-hours.

Finding a fresh spring of water, they decided to rest and sleep. Gilgamesh threw off his tunic, the gift of his ancestor, and bathed himself in the pool. As he stepped out clean and refreshed he saw a serpent at his feet. The creature grasped the magic plant and slithered off through the grass. Gilgamesh pursued it with loud cries and shouts. But the snake entered a hole in the earth and went underground, leaving behind only the old and withered skin that it had dropped in regaining its youth.

Gilgamesh beat his breast; he wrung his hands. "O Urshanabi, for whom have my hands become tired, my cheeks wan? For whom is my blood spent? For a snake! For an earth-prowler! O my magic weed, O my flower! Who will bring them back to me from under the earth? Why didn't I leave them at the quay of the carpenter!"

They walked through three settings and risings of the sun. They came to the river Euphrates and washed their hands in its water. Above them loomed the towered temples and the high walls of Uruk. "Come, Urshanabi!" Gilgamesh began to run.

He made Urshanabi climb the walls with him. "Behold," he said, "is it not the noblest of cities? Observe the walls if they be not made all of fired bricks! Inspect them, how they are moulded together; note the foundation terrace! Look out over the extent of the city, O boatman, see how it is arranged, one-third being houses and dwellings, one-third groves of trees and one-third the precinct of the temples! Judge for yourself now if it was not laid out by The Seven Wise Men!"

Gilgamesh At Last Finds Enkidu

They descended into the city and were at once surrounded by the populace who crowded close to them, grasping the hands of their king, embracing him, asking him questions. "What new adventures had he undergone? What new deeds would add to his glory?" They looked at Urshanabi with great curiosity, wondering about his strange looks, fingering his garments from a faraway time and an almost-forgotten place. A holiday was called and again there was feasting throughout the city of Uruk.

Ninsun had dressed herself in mourning during the absence of Gilgamesh. Now she put on garments of white and adorned herself in the rarest jewels. "Gilgamesh! You have come back and you still live! Have you come face to face with your ancestor, Utnapishtim? Have you found what you were seeking? Is your restless heart at last content?"

Gilgamesh told her about all his wanderings while she sat wide-eyed. He told her of how he had crossed the mountains of Mashu and then come face to face with great Shamash, the sun. He told her of how he had been treated kindly by the wine maiden, but ridiculed by his ancestor, Utnapishtim, the distant. Sadly he spoke of the magic weed called "The-Old-Become-Young-Again" and of how a snake had seized it and taken it underground. And Urshanabi was his witness.

"I have still one more undertaking, dear Ninsun," Gilgamesh said to his mother. "I must find Enkidu."

"O Gilgamesh, cease your running hither and thither! Stay in Uruk, my son; take a wife. Have a child that you can lead by the hand. Such is the conformity of life!"

"First, tell me what way to take, Mother. How shall I direct my steps to find my friend?"

Patient Ninsun mounted to the roof of her palace. She prepared incense and addressed herself to the god, Shamash, "Mighty Shamash, how shall my son direct his steps so that he may find his friend, Enkidu?"

The god replied, "Say this to Gilgamesh, that when he goes toward the gate of the underworld, he must discard his clean garments lest he arouse the envy of the dead. He must not wear sandals lest their noise arouse the sleeping. He must not carry a staff nor a spear lest he offend those who trembled before the staff, and anger those who fell before the spear. As to the path, I cannot say, for all my ways are the ways of light and I do not know the realms of darkness. Let him ask some other god."

Gilgamesh again said goodbye to his mother. Then, dressed in his royal tunic and golden sandals, with his spear on his back and his staff in his hand, he set out for Ekur, which is the house of the god Enlil. Standing before the door he cried out, "O Father Enlil, listen to me, Gilgamesh, who weep day and night for my friend and brother Enkidu. How can I make my way to him?"

The god Enlil did not answer him even by so much as a word.

He went to the house of the god Sin, who controlled the night and the moon. "O Father Sin, listen to me, Gilgamesh, who weep day and night for my friend and brother, Enkidu. How can I make my way to him?"

The god Sin did not reply.

with each other; they talked about everything they knew. "I will tell you of my wanderings, O Enkidu! I will tell you about Utnapishtim, my ancestor, and how he came to be set among the immortals. But first, tell me how it is with you! Tell me about the underworld where you dwell."

"Sit down and weep, my friend," said Enkidu. "Sit beside me and weep, for even as we talk together my body drops away like an old garment, and is filled with dust!"

Gilgamesh sat down and wept for his friend. Then he inquired, "How is it with kings in that world, Enkidu; have you seen them?"

"I have seen them," replied Enkidu. "The crowns of kings are laid on a shelf and their lot is that of serving-men."

"How is it with the hero who died in battle; have you seen him?"

"I have seen him; his father and his mother support his head, and his wife weeps over him."

"What of the man having a son; have you seen him?"

"I have seen him; one glass of water is his portion."

"What of the man who had two sons; have you seen him?"

"I have seen him; he has a house of bricks over his head and a loaf of bread each day!"

"What of the man who had three sons; have you seen him?"

"I have seen him; he is daily refreshed from the waterskins of the deep!"

"What of the man who had eight sons; have you seen him?"

"I have seen him; his name is blazoned upon standards of red and gold; his house is of stone, his image graven on it; daily he receives gifts and tributes!"

"And what of the man who had no son; have you seen him?"

"I have seen him; he lies unburied at the foot of the wall and cast-off crusts of bread are his portion!"

Gilgamesh then turned to Nergal, the gatekeeper and pleaded with him in this way: "Listen, gatekeeper, my brother Enkidu did not fall in battle; neither did he die of sickness or venerable old age. The earth came up and seized him; the underworld took him in the prime of his youth. Therefore release him! Let him return with me to Uruk-of-the-Walls that he may live out his life as a hero!"

But Nergal shook his head. "It is decreed, O Gilgamesh, that the dead may not join the living; the living only may join the dead!"

"As representative of the underworld, O gatekeeper, grant this plea to me, for I weep daily for my friend, Enkidu!"

"O Gilgamesh," said the gatekeeper, "you have come here dressed in a clean tunic which has excited the envy of the dead. You have come wearing sandals and thus aroused the sleeping from their sleep. You carry a staff in your hand and have offended those who trembled before the staff; your spear has angered those who fell by the spear. Therefore I cannot grant your plea!"

Gilgamesh grew fearful and turned to run from the field. He hesitated; after so many months of wandering and so much hardship, he had at last found Enkidu. Could he now desert him? Could he leave him behind and go back and live in the city? Had he found the life he sought, or love, or welcome at the quay of Utnapishtim?

He turned and walked toward his friend. He bowed; he fell into the dust among the weeds and bracken and the trailing vines of arbutus. Like a worm he lay on his face for seven days and seven nights while Enkidu knelt beside him. He was dead, and the earth reached up and seized him.

Thus Gilgamesh died, after all, a mortal's death. But even so, his life was not as an empty wind, for he made an everlasting name for himself. When he was gone the populace of Uruk mourned him, but at the same time they sang of his great deeds. Dancers acted out his adventures and his long quest; singers set them to music; and poets told them. Sculptors carved his face and his friend's face in stone; and painters covered the walls of houses and temples with the great story. Scribes wrote it all down on tablets of clay or rock. Uruk and its walls slowly crumbled and melted into the earth. Other cities and other languages came into being; but everywhere was repeated the name of Gilgamesh.

And when people heard the name and asked, "Who was this Gilgamesh?", they were answered:

> He who saw everything
> He who knew everything,
> He stood seven cubits high;
> Two-thirds of him was god,
> One-third of him was man;
> He was the most glorious of heroes,
> The most eminent of men,
> And Enkidu was his companion!

In Explanation

The legend of Gilgamesh is believed to be the first story written by man. Even before the invention of writing it is said to have been told from mouth to mouth and sung to the accompaniment of the harp.

When writing in wedge-shaped signs, called cuneiform, was first created by a people called the Sumerians—over three thousand years before the birth of Christ—the legend of Gilgamesh was duly recorded in that script. But the story was already a sophisticated one and must have been widely known.

Both the written script of the Sumerians and the story of Gilgamesh were taken over by other peoples. Akkadians, Babylonians, Assyrians, Hittites, and Persians were only a few of the peoples who learned to write their own tongues in the cuneiform script. The Sumerians and their language disappeared; their cities sank back into the earth, but the legend of Gilgamesh persisted.

It continued in many many versions, sometimes almost unrecognizable as the story of Gilgamesh. The names of the heroes changed into names suitable for other peoples. But at the same time, the story was preserved in its earliest forms in the great libraries of kings. Through some three millennia of time the countries of the Near East knew the myth of Gilgamesh and Enkidu.

Slowly it disappeared leaving its threads and traces everywhere, in biblical literature, in Egyptian lore, and throughout Greek mythology. Some people claim to find its imprint even in the beliefs of the early tribes of Britain.

The rediscovery of the ancient cities with their sculpture, their pottery, their objects in gold and silver, and the strange clay tablets with their curious markings is a wonderful epic in itself. The slow recognition that these markings were writing, that the writing recorded not just one but several languages, and that it contained a vast unknown literature is one of the great adventures of all time.

The tablets were slowly, laboriously deciphered. And among the other great secrets about mankind that were revealed was that of the epic of Gilgamesh. The scholars have, from the beginning, disagreed about the meanings of the story. And of course, new discoveries have constantly enriched it and supplied missing material. Thus there have been almost as many versions of it as there have been decipherers and translators.

This myth has been for me, a sort of delightful preoccupation ever since the late twenties when I first became familiar with it. I have followed its ins and outs, its ups and downs, as new discoveries seemed to shed light on its still persisting mysteries. Thus I have read text after text and noted not only that they differ from each other radically, but that there does emerge from all of them some current, like a deep underground river, that seems almost to overwhelm the notes, the interpretations and the explanations, and to constitute an epic greater than any of its versions.

I have tried to tell the story as simply as possible because I feel that it ought to be made accessible to young people. It is particularly theirs. In doing so I have not followed any single translation, nor have I tried to piece together several such versions. It has seemed better to me just to set down the story as I know it through so many readings, allowing all the surmises and the notions that I have had about it to take their place. Certainly, this is a highly personal account of the legend of Gilgamesh, but it adheres scrupulously to what I myself believe to be that story.

Bernarda Bryson

ABOUT THE PICTURES

The pictures accompanying the story of Gilgamesh have been suggested in very large part by the actual relics that have come to us from the time when that legend was current.

The relics are of all sorts—sculptures and bas-reliefs, fragments of painted walls, modeled and painted pottery, jewelry, temple objects, and vast architectural ruins. Listed below are some of the relics that have been translated into pictures to complement the story.

Page 5. The picture of a man hugging two bulls is suggested by figures inlaid in shell on the sound-box of a harp. This is of the early third millennium before Christ and is now in the museum of the University of Pennsylvania.

Page 10. The map of "The World of Gilgamesh" is actually the world of Sargon the Great who lived during the second millennium before Christ. It shows the "Bitter River" and the districts beyond, "where the sun is no longer seen," the salt swamp from which the animals arose, the Mountains of Mashu, the city of Babylon, and the Euphrates River. It was discovered in the library of Ashurbanipal who lived during the seventh century before Christ.

Page 11. The figure of Shamash stepping over the mountain to bring daylight to the world is from a cylinder seal of the middle third millennium before Christ.

Page 13. The company of worshipful elders is suggested by a collection of small sculptures found at a site called Mari in present-day Syria, and at Tell Asmar in Iraq.

Page 18. The struggle of Enkidu with the lion is drawn from the multitude of cylinder seals that deal with mythological themes—especially with the combats of Gilgamesh and Enkidu with wild beasts and with each other. Many such seals go back to more than four thousand years before Christ, and antedate writing itself. These seals are small cylinders of stone in which tableaux are carved in reverse, so that as they are rolled over soft clay a clear print remains in relief, and may be repeated as often as the cylinder is rolled. Often carved in the most precious stones, the seals served as personal signatures and were then, as they are now, prized as small treasures.

Other pictures derived from the seals are on pages 34, 41, 54, and 83. The figure of Shamash, mentioned above, as well as that on page 96 of the god, Ea, in his house of water are from seals. The farmhouse on page 20, the winged gate on page 41, and the attitudes of the gods on pages 9, 82, and 84 are details from cylinder seals.

Page 22. The dainty little priestess is suggested by one of the many and varied representations of the goddess, Ishtar. The bas-relief from which this comes shows the goddess just in this attitude, walking and smelling a flower.

Page 25. The figures and the garments of Enkidu and of the priestess Harim are suggested by a statue of an embracing couple found at Mari and believed to be of the middle third millennium before Christ. The faces here are suggested by those in a bas-relief of a man and wife gazing at each other. It is of the second millennium before Christ and is now in the Louvre.

Page 29. The figure of Ninsun is almost a portrait of a small statue of an ancient queen that was unearthed at Mari and is of the third millennium before Christ.

Pages 30-31. The pillars of the temple of the dream of Gilgamesh are suggested by low columns inlaid with colored cone-shaped mosaics that were uncovered in the ancient city of Uruk, and are thought to date back to some four thousand years before the time of Christ.

Pages 32, 80, and 99. The many scenes of people walking as though along sidewalks are suggested by the famous "Standard of Ur." This object, probably itself carried in processions, is composed of figures in shell inlaid in lapis-lazuli. On one side are shown military figures, kings, and chariots; on the other are common citizens at their day-to-day work. One man walks with an enormous fish on his head; another carries a crated package. Still another leads sheep through the streets, another cattle, and still another tenderly carries along a baby goat. In one corner a man walks playing a large harp and is followed by a woman singing. Several citizens are seated and drinking as though at sidewalk cafes. The figures on this beautiful object give the impression of a busy, un-oppressed, and rather happy citizenry. The Ur standard, now in the British Museum, is believed to be from the early third millennium before Christ.

Pages 49, 90-91 and jacket. The pictures of temples emulate the soft, curving, and irregular lines that are seen in the ancient ruins rather than the severe ones of the more scientific models that have been reconstructed in recent times.

Page 43. The face of Humbaba follows closely a terra-cotta mask of this demon made during the second millennium before Christ.

Page 45. The head of the goddess, Ishtar, is crowned, not by the usual headdress of goddesses, but by that of the great queen Shub-ad who was buried in the royal cemetery at Ur together with her jewels, her golden harp, and two hundred and seventy priceless objects of gold, silver, and precious stones. She lived and died some five thousand years ago.

Page 85. The attitude of this figure of Ishtar, holding her jewels before her, comes from a bas-relief from a site called Ischali, in Iraq.

Page 101. Here are shown some of the ways of burying the dead in ancient Sumer.

The above notes describe only a few of the ancient relics from which pictures and details of pictures have been taken. A few words in cuneiform have been used here and there, to give the reader some sense of the look of the written language.

Thus, on page 9, the cuneiform line under the picture of the gods is *Igigi*, meaning the spirits of Heaven.

On page 11, the small figure below the god is simply the name, Shamash.

On page 12, is the name of the god, Anu; and on page 32 (above) is the name Enkidu, and (below) Gilgamesh.

On page 81, is *Annunaki,* that is, the demons of the earth and of the elements.

On page 96, is the name of the god, Ea; and on page 103, Nergal, keeper of the underworld.

BERNARDA BRYSON began to write as early as she can remember, and by the age of twelve, had vast sheaves of manuscripts. She also drew continually as a child, in whatever empty space she could find – especially on the fly leaves of books and her mother's sheets of music. After attending college in Ohio, when Miss Bryson began to work, her "vocational schizophrenia" reflected her dual childhood interests, but after moving back and forth between writing and illustration, she gradually became more completely devoted to drawing, print-making and illustrating. For many years she was occupied in magazine illustration for *Harpers, Scientific American, Fortune,* and others.

Miss Bryson began to illustrate children's books as a result of enjoying doing *The Twenty Miracles of Saint Nicolas,* which she wrote and illustrated. She combined her two great interests again in *The Zoo of Zeus,* an adult book, and GILGAMESH. Miss Bryson has also done distinguished illustrations for children's books of other authors. Her illustrations for *The Sun Is a Golden Earring* by Natalia Belting were honored as runner-up for the 1963 Caldecott Award.

Miss Bryson believes that illustration is the illumination of a text and calls on every facet of one's experience. While her text of GILGAMESH represents many years' reading and probing, her illustrations also draw upon an enormous wealth of archeological material. "The content of the pictures is very much the content of the ancient clay tablets, sculptures, terra cottas and gold and bronze pieces of two thousand to thirty-five hundred years before Christ. I have tried to impart the incredible fantasies that ran through their art."

She resides in Roosevelt, New Jersey, with her husband, the noted artist, Ben Shahn.